First published in Great Britain in 2004 by Zero To Ten Limited,
part of the Evans Publishing Group
2a Portman Mansions
Chiltern Street
London W1U 6NR

A CIP catalogue record for this book is available from the British Library
Got, Yves
Louie's Little Zoo
1. (Fictitious character) - Pictorial works
Juvenile literature 2. Antonyms - Pictorial works
Juvenile literature 3. Polarity - Pictorial works
Juvenile literature
I. Title
428.1

ISBN 1-84089-316-8

Printed and bound in Singapore.

Louie's Little Zoo

Yves Got

ZERO TO TEN

dog

ladybird

goldfish

canary

cat

tortoise

snail

hen

cockerel

chick

goose

duck

ducklings

pig

peacock

pigeon

rabbit

guinea fowl

turkey

sheep

lamb

donkey

horse

COW

bull

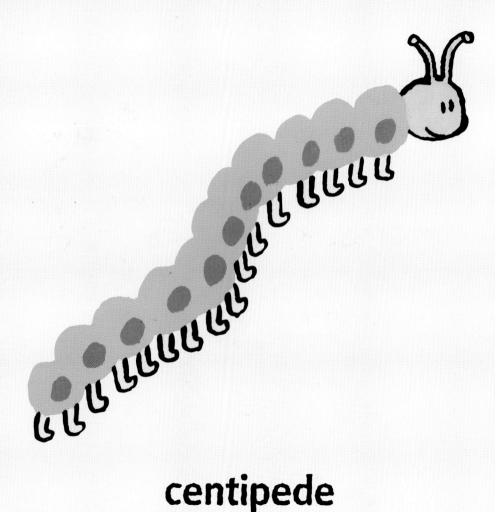

centipede

butterfly

dragonfly

stork

lizard

mouse

bat

mole

hedgehog

spider

squirrel

woodpecker

fox

koala

wild boar

owl

deer

panda

flamingo

swan

fly

frog

kingfisher

crane

beaver

crocodile

hippopotamus

gorilla

chameleon

jaguar

panther

anteater

toucan

parrot

monkey

tiger

camel with two humps

camel with one hump

vulture

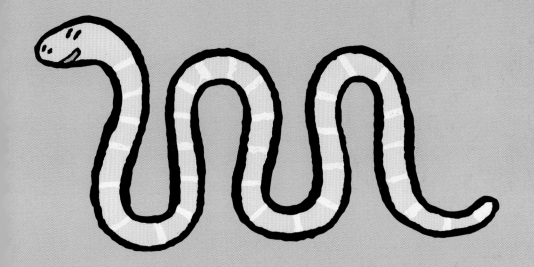

snake

whale

seagull

pelican

crab

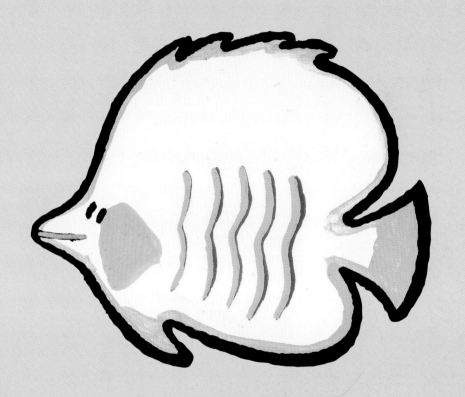

tropical fish

octopus

dolphin

shark

lion

elephant

giraffe

zebra

leopard

antelope

rhinoceros

ostrich

bison

kangaroo

crow

buffalo

brown bear

wolf

llama

eagle

St Bernard dog

goat

walrus

polar bear

penguin

seal

moose

reindeer

dinosaur

mammoth

Animal Quiz
Where do we live?

Can you match the different animals to their homes?

Animals

dog	cow	frog
ladybird	bull	fly
goldfish	centipede	kingfisher
canary	butterfly	crane
cat	dragonfly	beaver
tortoise	stork	crocodile
snail	lizard	hippopotamus
hen	mouse	gorilla
chick	bat	chameleon
cockerel	mole	jaguar
goose	hedgehog	panther
duck	spider	anteater
pig	squirrel	toucan
peacock	woodpecker	parrot
pigeon	fox	monkey
rabbit	koala	tiger
guinea fowl	wild boar	camel
turkey	owl	vulture
sheep	deer	snake
lamb	panda	whale
donkey	flamingo	seagull
horse	swan	pelican

crab	rhinoceros	goat
tropical fish	ostrich	walrus
octopus	bison	polar bear
dolphin	kangaroo	penguin
shark	crow	seal
lion	buffalo	moose
elephant	brown bear	reindeer
giraffe	wolf	dinosaur
zebra	llama	mammoth
leopard	eagle	
antelope	St Bernard dog	

Homes

Which animals live...

in the garden?

in the desert?

in or by the sea?

in or by a river?

in or by a lake?

on the plains?

in the savanna?

in the mountains?

at home?

on the farm?

in the countryside?

in the jungle?

at the North or South Pole?

Remember some animals can live in more than just one place and one or two might even be extinct!

Index